THE DRAWINGS OF
ANTONIO GAUDI

George R. Collins

March 26—May 24, 1977

This exhibition is made possible in part
through public funds received from the
New York State Council on the Arts

Presented under the sponsorship of the
Consulate General of Spain in New York

THE DRAWING CENTER

Designed, edited, and produced by James Hoekema
Typeset by Cardinal Type Service
Printed by Sterling-Roman Press

Cover: Study of the façade of the Casa Battló (Cat. No. 105, detail).
Back cover: Gaudí's signature as printed on his business card (Cat. No. 36).
Frontispiece: Photograph of Gaudí in the procession of the Corpus in Barcelona, taken about 1925.
Photograph Credits: David Allison, New York (4, 5, 11, 13, 15, 100, 127, 128, 130, cover); Foto Medrano, Barcelona (6, 18, 106, 121, 123, 131); Foto Archivo Brangulí (frontispiece). Figs. 1 and 3 are taken from Ráfols, *Gaudí* (1929), pp. 226–27. Figs. 2 and 4 courtesy Amigos de Gaudí, Barcelona. Fig. 5 courtesy Archivo Mas, Barcelona.

THE DRAWING CENTER
137 Greene Street, New York, N.Y. 10012
A nonprofit center for the study and exhibition of drawings.
Directors:
Edward H. Tuck, Chairman; Martha Beck, Colin Eisler, John B. Hightower, Stephen J. Hoffman, Douglas Newton, Dorothea Rockburne.

CONTENTS

ACKNOWLEDGMENTS

The following are the individuals who graciously loaned or made possible the loan of drawings and other materials included in the exhibition.

Professor Juan Bassegoda Nonell

Sra. doña María Boyer, Vda. Llensa, Barcelona

Sr. Miquel Brullet i Monmany, Arquitecte, Mataró

Ilmo. Sr. Dr. D. Javier de Cárdenas Chávarri, Director de la Escuela Técnica Superior de Arquitectura de Barcelona

Rev. P.D. Régulo Casas, Pbro., Párroco de Santa Coloma de Cervelló

Sr. Don Emilio Hurtado Llamas, Presidente del Patronato de la Caja de Ahorros y Monte de Piedad de León

Mr. Thaddeus E. Kusmierski, Architect, Berkeley, California

Ilmo. Sr. Don José Francisco Llevat Briansó, Alcalde de Reus

Ilmo. Sr. Don Jorge Mir Valls, Decano del Colegio Oficial de Arquitectos de Cataluña y Baleares, Barcelona

Rev. P. Fortià Pietx, Pvere., Rector de Sant Feliu d'Alella, Alella

Rvdo. P. Don Augusto Quintana Prieto, Pbro., Director del Museo de los Caminos, Astorga

Ilmo. Sr. Don Francisco Sala Morat, Alcalde de Mataró

Excmo. Sr. Don José María Socías Humbert, Alcalde de Barcelona

Sr. Don Edmundo Vidal, Barcelona

FOREWORD

The Drawing Center takes great pleasure in presenting this exhibition of drawings by the great Catalan architect Antonio Gaudí. Initiating what will become a series devoted to architectural drawings, this is the first exhibition of Gaudí's drawings ever held in this country, and the second and largest to be mounted anywhere—the first being the display in June 1976 in Barcelona of about fifty drawings, most of which are included in the present exhibition.

All those who have worked on the exhibition are deeply indebted to its guest curator, George R. Collins, Professor of Art History at Columbia University and author of numerous books and articles on Gaudí, including a portfolio of the drawings to be published by Princeton University Press. Christiane C. Collins also provided invaluable assistance in making arrangements in Spain. We are particularly grateful to Professor Juan Bassegoda, holder of the Gaudí chair at the School of Architecture in Barcelona and president of the Amigos de Gaudí, who from the beginning helped plan the exhibition and provided indispensable support throughout its preparation. Thanks are also due to His Excellency Alberto Lopez Herce, Consul General of Spain; Jorge Dezcallar, Cultural Counselor, Deputy Consul General of Spain; and the Chancellor Mrs. Carmella García-Verdugo. Finally, the gratitude of all those involved in the project goes out to the lenders, who graciously consented to part . with their much-loved and irreplaceable drawings by Gaudí in order to make this exhibition possible.

I wish to thank the entire staff of the Drawing Center, with particular appreciation to Marie Therese Keller, Registrar, and to Jerry Gorovoy, who measured most of the drawings for the catalogue. I would also like to express my gratitude to James Hoekema, who edited, designed, and produced the catalogue in the extraordinary period of three weeks. His thanks and ours also go to Randall DeLeeuw, Bert Clarke, Marlene Rothkin Vine, and Tim McDonough, as well as to David Allison for photography.

On a more personal level, I would add that Gaudí seems to have attracted scholars and admirers of unusual grace, perception, and enthusiasm. The pleasure of working with them only adds to the excitement of the subject itself, Gaudí's drawings.

Martha Beck, Director
The Drawing Center

PREFACE

This is a most improbable exhibition. To begin with, until recently it was thought that virtually all of the drawings of Antonio Gaudí had perished in the incidents of 1936 in Catalonia, and his drawings, when studied, were dealt with by means of old photographs or pictures printed before that date. However, the investigative zeal of several of his admirers, in particular the late Enric Casanelles, the late César Martinell, and more recently Professor Juan Bassegoda of the Barcelona School of Architecture has brought to light more than 100 drawings during the past decade or so, among them examples of nearly every type of drawing he did and of each of his graphic styles. Although it is quite common for architects to dispose periodically of their drawings, Gaudí did not do so, and we know that when he died in 1926 there were hundreds in the bulging files of his atelier at the Sagrada Familia church and more than 500 at his residence in the Park Güell, plus an unknown quantity at the church of the Colonia Güell, outside Barcelona. All of these perished, which is why we have so little on exhibit related to his two famous unfinished churches.

And who, then, would believe that these now priceless fragments of the vigorous Catalan Renaixensa movement of the late 19th and early 20th century that are scattered about the Spanish peninsula in the spots where they had escaped destruction would ever be seen all together in New York City? As Gaudí has always meant so much to the Catalans, and today to all Spaniards, I doubted whether the drawings could be procured for exhibition outside of Spain. But their owners proved to be very cooperative for the most part, and through the efforts of Professor Bassegoda, who had actually made the greatest number of new finds, I was able to bring most of the extant works back with me from a recent trip to Spain; the rest followed by diplomatic pouch soon afterwards, thanks to the efforts of the Spanish Consulate General in New York City.

Most of the drawings here exhibited bear Gaudí's signature, and many are obviously by his hand alone. His was a close-knit atelier, however, and associated with him were architects and other artists of independent stature who carried out parts of his construction and his drawings—sometimes perceptibly. There were a dozen or so of these of overlapping generations, and sometimes their work has been confused with Gaudí's. We exhibit a house, for instance, by his young townsman and collaborator Domingo Sugrañes—a drawing generously sent us by its owner. We did not request from Spain a famous sketch of the baldacchino for the Cathedral of Mallorca which I am convinced is totally by his associate José María Jujol who supervised Gaudí's work there. A number of the drawings on linen are clearly shopwork, and we also exhibit a few projects that are too humdrum for Gaudí even to have designed but are signed by him—a common custom—for various close friends.

As regards the quantities of Gaudí's surviving drawings: Approximately 20 are from his days in architectural school, relating to about eight different projects. There are 80 to 90 drawings of buildings actually constructed of which a dozen of the buildings stand, a half-dozen are destroyed. Another half-dozen drawings are of unexecuted works, and about 20 are of objects and other non-architectural things. With a few exceptions these extant drawings are here, and we have put all but a few redundant ones on exhibit. About 50 other drawings are documented from printed sources or old photographs. In all, we know of about 200 Gaudí drawings, of which over half are currently on exhibit.

Portions of this catalogue have been adapted from the text of a forthcoming portfolio of Gaudí designs and drawings—devoted to all original drawings about which anything at all is known, and illustrated also with modern measured drawings of several major buildings—which has been in preparation for some time by Professor Bassegoda and myself for the Princeton University Press. The present catalogue is an almost complete inventory of Gaudí's actually extant drawings.

George R. Collins
March 1977

GAUDI'S DRAWINGS
AND MANNER OF WORKING

Antonio Gaudí used a wide variety of drawings and models in order to conceptualize architectural problems and to design his solutions to them. Some of his procedures are probably unique in history and go a long way to explain the unusual nature and appearance of his works.

In order to understand his design procedures and working methods—especially those peculiar to him—it would be useful to point out some general principles that are observable in his architecture.

The works of Gaudí are almost alone in the history of architecture for their quality of identity between form and structure. In them the structure *is* the form, and the forms are structural. The forms of his architecture are also geometrical in appearance and are controlled by geometrical laws. This is itself common in architecture, but Gaudí's mature architecture is uncommon, indeed prophetic, in the fact that its geometry consists of ruled surfaces of double curvature (paraboloids, hyperboloids, helicoids, etc.) which he considered to be a geometry that underlies nature's forms and structures and thus to comprise realistic forms, not artificial abstractions.

From early in his career, although the actual forms were to change considerably, Gaudí sought what came to be called "equilibrated" structures, that is, masonry structures (i.e., brick or stone) that are self-sufficient within themselves and are composed of units that are likewise self-sufficient: no props, no buttresses. This was like the principle of "equilibrium" attributed to Gothic buildings by Eugène Viollet-le-Duc (whom Gaudí much admired) and is described in the article on "Construction" in Viollet-le-Duc's *Dictionnaire*. For Gaudí, however, the equilibrium of Gothic cathedrals was implied rather than actual: without their buttresses they would collapse. Gaudí was derogatory about Gothic architecture, calling it "incomplete" and "industrial." He often spoke of his own work as Greek, which it certainly did not resemble, although the internal contrapposto of a classic Greek statue does indeed have the sense of "equilibrium" that he pursued. Characteristically, Gaudí found this equilibrium most clearly in nature.

"Would you like to know what my model has been?" Pointing to a eucalyptus tree in front of his studio, Gaudí answered his own question: "A straight-standing tree; it supports its branches, and these the twigs, and these the leaves. And everything grows harmoniously, grandly, since God

Himself is the artist who created it. The tree does not need external support. Everything in it is balanced in itself. Everything is in equilibrium.''

Many of the idiosyncratic features of his architecture are related to this search: parabolic arches, mushroom capitals, corbeled supporting members, thin low-rise cohesive vaults of insignificant lateral thrust, *inclined columns*. He commented: ''Have you ever observed that when one leans on a cane one inclines it? Thus my inclined columns are stone canes in which, as is obvious, the technique of following the lines and curves of forces is even more refined.''

Perhaps Gaudí's most frequently quoted statement—and his cryptic utterances have always been treated like those of a Wise Man or guru—is: ''Originality is to return to the origin.'' This can mean many things, but with respect to his designing it seems to imply a return to the binary origins of everything that is: Nature and Geometry.

The drawings of an architect, in addition to their innate qualities as objects of art, tell us much about his methods of working. Let us look at Gaudí's drawings from two points of view: how they functioned in his conceptualization of buildings, built or unbuilt, and what they reveal of the chronological development of his aesthetic ideas.

It must be borne in mind that for Gaudí a *sketch* was only one of several devices for analyzing a project, and a *presentation* drawing in no way committed him to carry out the building in exactly the form depicted. He insisted on visualizing the project in its entirety, as an existential whole, by one method or another. In his later career he relied more and more on models and mockups to do this; in a sense his drawings became a preliminary, or a supplement, or merely a two-dimensional projection of the idea for the benefit of his public. For one reason or another, then, drawings by Gaudí often bear an ambiguous relationship to the building as it stands.

Gaudí's drawings are extremely varied in character and in medium. They are executed on a variety of papers. They include crumpled notes, sketches on the back of calling cards and on the face of photographs; they range from tiny sketches to huge working drawings. He drew with pencil, charcoal, India ink, pastel, and watercolor. We have a detail of the Sagrada Familia church on a block of building stone, in the manner of medieval master masons. As preparation for sculpture he used snapshots and various multiple-exposure and multi-view photographs; as models for architecture *and* sculpture he employed metal armatures, wire mesh, plaster or clay maquettes, paper or cloth constructions, string or wire nets, flexible human skeletons of either bone or metal, plaster casts of objects, and casts taken from living humans and animals. With certain devices like the suspended funicular models for buildings, the study of skeletons in movement, and the life casts for sculpture he considered himself to be following ancient traditions, but it is unlikely that anyone had ever before tried to duplicate so exactly Nature's laws and appearances.

So it is that in the period of Gaudí's mature architecture such drawings as we possess give us only a partial or fragmentary insight into his conceptualizing processes. To analyze by means of only his sketches and working drawings the design procedures of a man who was famous for working from three-dimensional models and by directions and indications on the site is, admittedly, inadequate.

But even if we did have at hand the large mass of drawings that Gaudí left behind in 1926, we would still be hampered by the relative lack of serious and art-historical studies of other architects' drawings to use for comparison. Even in the case of such artists as Raphael, Bernini, or Otto Wagner, whose graphic works have been well published, architectural drawings have tended to be employed more as documents for the chronology of building programs than for their own artistic style and merits. With Gaudí we have a further handicap that little attention has been paid to the drawing styles of his teachers, his contemporaries, and his substantial associates. At various times a good deal of Gaudí's originality has been attributed to one or another of his close associates, but although it may be that Gaudí could never have accomplished what he did without them (he eulogized Francisco Berenguer as his "right arm"), there is no evidence that any or all of them could have done what he did without him.

The drawings by Gaudí that are preserved fall quite easily into several classes, and it is likely that the lost ones could also have been categorized the same way.

There are his school projects (Nos. 3–9, 11–15) which were carried out in the familiar Beaux-Arts system of first a qualifying sketch (*esquisse*) and then the follow-up of elaborate plans, sections, elevations, details.

There is a considerable group that can be called "official," that is, they were prepared in the course of seeking legal permission to erect a commissioned building. These can in turn be divided into different types. There are land surveys such as No. 1 (done as a student), two recently discovered property surveys in the countryside of Catalonia (not requested for the exhibition), and the various Park Güell layouts of which we exhibit a blueprint (No. 102). In Catalonia the local administration seemed to be interested only in whether a building conformed to its building ordinances in the grossest features: height, overhang, window arrangement, light courts, etc.—in other words, its envelope. To satisfy such requirements Gaudí prepared for submission with applications plans, sections, and elevations of barest linear outline. Those for the Casa Vicens (Nos. 39–46), Badía workshop (No. 104), Casa Batlló (Nos. 106–09), and Casa Milá (Nos. 120–26) are good examples. These outline drawings are of little value to us except as documents and as Gaudí's own representation of his style of composing major architectural elements at that time. Indeed, some we suspect that he did not even design or draw but only signed as a courtesy to friends (Nos. 80–87). In some cases he was obliged to prepare more scrupulously exact renderings, for example, in order to pass the scrutiny of the Real Academia de San Fernando in Madrid regarding the Bishop's Palace in Astorga (Nos. 60–68). In this case the examiners gave him considerable trouble, and it is amusing to see that for all the details he included, the resultant building bears very little relation to his promised designs. His rather careful drawings for the Casa Calvet in Barcelona, especially No. 88, are also an example of this last type.

Another major class would be the presentation drawings that he prepared for his intended clients. These were more meticulous and often sumptuous, for obvious reasons. Examples include the Girosi kiosk (No. 18), the Mataró Social Center (Nos. 25–26), the Alella altar (No. 38), the Tangier Missions (No. 79), and the Casa Batlló (No. 105).

A fourth class of drawings consists of those, not necessarily architectural, that might be called "personal." Where they are of commissioned projects they appear to be preliminary or supplementary sketches, studies that record certain ideas and functions—i.e., pictorial notations. For instance, there are some very early lost exercises of which we have evidence, and there are the doodles in his school notebooks (No. 130). Another category would be his freehand sketches of non-architectural subjects (Nos. 2, 31, 129, 132–38). And lastly there are the study sketches for specific structures: the Comella showcase (No. 17), the Muralla de Mar perspective (No. 36). Later this type of sketch seems to become more central for him—we know that at work he was accustomed to draw rapidly on octavo-size paper that he carried in his pocket—and the sketch then embodies much of the spirit of his mature architectural style. An example is the Reus sanctuary (No. 100); one should also mention the sketches he made on photographs, for example for the Colonia Güell church (Nos. 127–28).

Finally there is a miscellany that might loosely be called "working drawings." These would include the few actual working drawings that have survived, namely those for León (Nos. 71–78). There are also graphic statics studies, including a remarkable set for the ramp of the Colonia Güell church (loan refused). We presume that many of the working drawings and presentation drawings were executed in part by assistants like Rubió and Berenguer. The sculptor Juan Matamala, who in his youth assisted Gaudí in many tasks, tells us that the most used working drawings (those for the Sagrada Familia towers) were not only soiled but had many lightly traced additions by both Gaudí and his assistants.

We can perhaps best visualize Gaudí's method of "drawing" and projecting his ideas by examining the system that he used for the Sagrada Familia church. He had his assistants construct an inclined platform of wood on which they mounted life-size plaster elements of the Nativity façade; he directed this process from a type of pulpit set up at the bottom end. Once so composed, the model was then taken apart, and the individual pieces were installed in their proper locations on the façade (we have old photographs of this), later to be substituted for, piece by piece, by definitive stone sculptures. When construction of the façade reached the height of the towers, Gaudí ordered the architect Quintana and others to prepare huge scale drawings of the pinnacles. The papers for these drawings were extended on the floor, where the assistants worked, stooped over them. Later Gaudí inspected the lines; when he found any that he considered defective, he would scratch them out with his cane. This meant that they had to be redrawn on another piece of paper and then patched onto the torn piece. When the temporary plaster sculptures were inserted in the Nativity façade, Gaudí would supervise from across the street, calling for corrections by his assistants, the sculptors Mani, Matamala, and Vilarrubias, if the perspective effect was faulty when seen from below. He frequently used plaster maquettes to study portions of his architecture; a scale model of the Casa Milá stood in the attic of that building until the early 1950s.

In order to study the stylistic properties of Gaudí's drawings as works of art and as illustrations of his constantly modifying aesthetic ideas, let us examine them chronologically.

Although he seems always to have experienced some difficulty with the human figure, Gaudí's design projects done in architectural school reveal him to be already an accomplished draftsman who showed an admirable grasp of the total sense, or sentiment, of the project in which he was involved. From this point on Gaudí sees architectural design as a holistic effort; each set of renderings is quite different, presumably because each problem was, at root, distinct, and each is charged with an intangible atmosphere that is its own. The range of focus is from precise, close detail to dreamy, romantic background. In his diary of these years he was to write on the subject of "Understanding the Object; Freehand Drawing" that "Given the matter, it is necessary to study it and understand it, purging it of all that is superfluous, and once it has been carefully set forth with all its difficulties and inconveniences, we will proceed to attempt to apply form to the idea, always tending toward a simplified form, but giving satisfaction to the artistic conception, and not letting go of it until all of the difficulties of structure, form, plan, facilities, etc. have been solved."

With his project of the year 1876, the patio of a Provincial Diputación (No. 4), we see for the first time a specific manner, the neo-grec, that is to mark his early works, probably because he learned it at the school or as draftsman to one or another of the several men he assisted on the outside. (Neo-grec is not neoclassical in the ordinary sense of solid classic forms, but was an international decorative style of the nineteenth century characterized by linear and arabesque forms, often incised, seemingly derived from ancient Greek ornamental motifs.) The rendering of the fence and gate that we understand him to have done for Fontseré at that time (No. 16) is a marvel of fantasizing on the motifs of the neo-grec. The turned, jointed, chamfered treatment of the metallic elements in both the student project and the executed gate is quite characteristic, as are the machined forms that he gives the metal attachments in comparison with the firm ashlar stone.

The element of fantasy seems to increase during Gaudí's school years and is particularly striking in his final exercise in design: a large academic meeting hall or "Paraninfo" (Nos. 11–15). Also present here is a Moslem ingredient, important among architects of the new Catalan "Renaixensa" style of the day—struggling as they were out of the long tyranny of academic neoclassical form. It is usually referred to as Mudéjar, a term that had recently been invented by scholars for archaeological purposes but which nevertheless properly refers to Spanish-Moslem eclecticism of any period. Apart from its specific stylistic elements, largely ornamental, the Mudéjar seems at all times to have represented an especially luxurious life-style to which Christian Spaniards aspired—whether they were the petty nobility of the later Middle Ages or the upper middle class of late 19th-century Catalonia. Both Gaudí's patron Manuel Vicens and the Royal Family of Spain, among others, had a Moslem *fumador* or smoking room designed for their residences, Vicens' being more modest, but thanks to Gaudí, more original than that in the Royal Palace at Aranjuez. The scale and the spatial span of the Paraninfo, as well as its stepped pyramidal roof surmounted by a large temple structure (No. 13), also suggest that Gaudí was still fascinated by the visionary manner of French Romantic Classicism which had been popular among older Catalan architects during Gaudí's youth.

But picking out stylistic details in the work of Gaudí is not as productive as studying the ultimate, total effect that he conveys. In this case he has pictured an immense, dramatically lit interior with sparkling surfaces, a make-believe world not unlike that produced in works of the painter Gustave Moreau. In the monochrome *esquisse* for this project (No. 11) the sense of atmosphere is given differently, by loosely enveloping pencil strokes and a lancing shorthand—examples of the nervous line by which Gaudí will always set out his first ideas. This type of agitated, sometimes spikey line can also be seen in his sketches for decorative medallions for another school project (No. 2).

Gaudí's drawings in architectural school tell us a great deal; it is no wonder that he asked for them after graduation and treasured them himself, or that they were later recalled by the school to be exhibited there. (Through some bureaucratic error they were not returned to him and were thus saved, to be found in rolls only recently by Professor Bassegoda.) The school sketches reveal Gaudí's brio and his idiosyncratic drawing style; the finished renderings testify to his meticulous, punctilious working method—his perfectionism. The buildings depicted contain within them many specific motifs that he would later use in executed works. The total effect is of a new and different world—an architect's paradise—that all his executed buildings will aspire to attain.

The few drawings that survive from Gaudí's first year out of school are similar. The Reliquary (No. 22) echoes the style of his monumental renderings; the tiny Comella sketch (No. 17) has his naturalistic wriggly lines; and the Mataró drawings (especially Nos. 24, 25), the Girosi kiosk (No. 18), and the Miró wall (No. 21) play with neo-grec motifs. Sometimes during these years the combination of washes and agitated line, as in the Girosi kiosk, remind one of the sketching style of his fellow townsman and painter Mariano Fortuny, whom Gaudí is known to have admired.

This almost neo-Rococo manner also characterizes the preliminary sketch and the renderings for a costume cavalcade at Vallfogona in 1879 (Nos. 31–35). It is interesting to compare the preliminary sketch (No. 31) with the four renderings that are in various stages of completeness and which draw variously on the single original sketch, all of them flattening out the composition to a shallow frieze-like motion without either the *repoussoir* figure, cast shadows, or the hint of hills in the distance. One assumes that the spikey, undated plant sketches in the Reus Museum (No. 132) are also of this time. The Muralla de Mar bird's-eye panorama sketch (No. 36) exhibits this piquant manner as well.

During the 1880s, from what evidence we have, Gaudí's manner of sketching and rendering tightened appreciably. It abandoned the flourishes and curlicues, and it solidified—comparable perhaps to the way in which his building designs began to deal with large masses and sub-units of distinctly geometrical character, omitting much of the finicky neo-grec decor and intaglio line of his early works. This is apparent in the renderings that we have for the Casa Vicens (Nos. 39–46), the Palacio Güell (47–52), and the Astorga palace (Nos. 60–68), although the simplification in the case of the Casa Vicens drawings can also be explained by what I have called their "official" purpose. But if one examines carefully either the Barcelona Cathedral façade (No. 37) or the Alella Chapel project (No. 38) of these years, it will be seen that the curling, agitated line persists within the stricter delineation of the large architectural forms and gives a sense of vitality to the whole.

This tendency towards a tighter style continues into the next decade, at least in his presentation drawings; that of the façade of the Casa de los Botines in León (No. 69) exemplifies this and is, furthermore, unique in the *oeuvre* of Gaudí in that the drawing actually looks like the building as finished, being different in only a few very minor details. The lettering is beginning to flow, however, in a calligraphy that is to be characteristic of Catalan Renaixensa graphics during the years that are marked by the Art Nouveau and Jugendstil elsewhere in Europe. The formal rendering of the Franciscan missions in Tangier (No. 79) exhibits a similar calligraphic style, and, if we can judge from the tiny photograph that survives, the building was rendered with a non-perspective frontality of façade with compacted receding sides, like León. Otherwise the Moroccan project is involved with wall surfaces resembling Gaudí's contemporaneous Teresan school and towers such as he was planning for the Sagrada Familia church. Labeling for the later Casa Calvet drawings (Nos. 88–98) is also of this style.

Shortly after 1900 a great change took place in Gaudí's art, which now took on that dynamic, flowing quality for which he is popularly known. Observable in many ways and an element of all the projects in which he was engaged, this quality can perhaps be most dramatically demonstrated in connection with later work he did at the Casa Calvet. The building itself was apparently finished in 1899. Sometime between 1901 and 1902 he designed

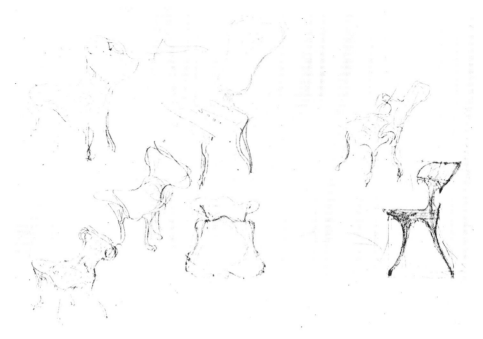

Fig. 1

the first of what we would today call ''free-form'' furniture for an office in the building. In a series of quick sketches (Fig. 1) which are unfortunately lost, we can see Gaudí reaching for the essential ''function'' of a chair as a support for the ''function'' of a human body at rest. The animality of the result (Fig. 2) should not surprise us; we know it in a more superficial way in contemporary Art Nouveau furniture that imitates the antelope or insect. A useful comparison at this point, which his biographer Ráfols also made (and thus ''saved'' these two lost drawings for us) is with a drawing that Gaudí made for a chair for himself in 1878 (Fig. 3) and which we can see has all the monumentality and mechanistic gadgetry that we associate with the taste of the Victorian period and that we have noted in the grandiose renderings for his architecture school courses. Gaudí's design ideas have in the Calvet chairs come down to earth—literally—and at the same time have become more totally spatial: this is as true of his drawing manner as of the objects portrayed or projected.

The drawing in our exhibition that partakes most thoroughly of this changed manner is that for the Sanctuary in Reus (No. 100). The more flowing of the two sketches on that sheet shows Gaudí working out solids, space, and ornament deftly and tentatively, as in the various alternative forms for the Calvet chairs. The two studies have much in common.

It also seems to have been in the first years of our century that Gaudí began the practice of sketching his ideas on top of existing images—a photograph, a measured drawing, or a graphic static by one of his own staff. The most famous of these are the sketches that he made, including our Nos.

Fig. 2   Fig. 3

127–28, on top of inverted photographs of the funicular model that he had had constructed in order to study the complex piers and vaults of the church for the Colonia Güell at Santa Coloma de Cervelló. The construction of the model is a story in itself for which he had prepared graphic static calculations, unfortunately not on exhibition, over which he made tentative sketches of final building forms. But the model of cords and weights, a multi-dimensional graphic static figure, he had draped with sheets so that it could be photographed for its forms rather than its string-lines of force (Figs. 5, 6). The idea of such a skeletal composition of cords supporting a plastic surface, is, of course, similar to the skeletal frame of the Calvet chairs, which support and cup the human body by means of wooden pads formed somewhat like a chalice. As he apparently kept re-adjusting the weights and cords of the funicular model and took a variety of photographs both inside and out from various points of view, he was provided with a large quantity of images on which to sketch his changing ultimate ideas of building form. These were tacked up on the walls of the workshed at the site, as recorded in an old photograph.

Another example of this tactic is the remarkable rendering for the Casa Batlló (No. 105) that turned up at the School of Architecture with Gaudí's course projects; apparently it had also been requested by the school for exhibit and was not returned to him. The Casa Batlló is a recycled building, and Gaudí drew the existing building—or had it drawn (I think that I see Berenguer's hand in the underwork)—and proceeded to draw over it, in some detail, his ideas about the new façade. This drawing not only testifies

19

 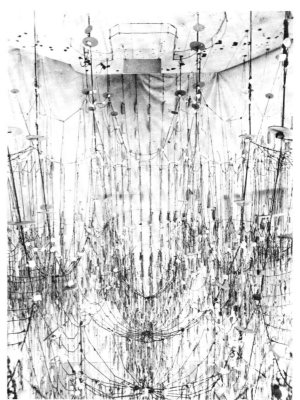

Fig. 4   Fig. 5

to the intense three-dimensionality and dynamism of his 20th-century works (we know that he also suggested architectural changes in the Barcelona skyline by drawing over a photographic view), but also reveals the ceaselessly transforming concepts that he had of all his current works. In spite of the care that he took with the rendering of the Batlló façade, he did not build it that way; his sketched-over forms are slightly more Baroque (like the Misericordia, No. 100) and are reminiscent of some just completed designs for a residence and the Park Güell. As built, the Casa Batlló was to have a pinnacle more like that in his later rendering for the Casa Milá (No. 121). But the Casa Milá, as built, had no such pinnacle and emphasized a somewhat different design including the famous chimney pots, not to be seen in No. 121. Even the tiniest details of his buildings seem to have undergone such a metamorphic process; for instance, Nos. 135–36 are two of a considerable series of studies for a monogram M, probably the one on the Casa Batlló pinnacle *as done*.

So the tragedy of the loss of Gaudí's drawings in 1936 is the more poignant. Clearly, it is impossible to chronicle the development of his architectural forms without simultaneous study of his drawings, especially because he would proceed to transform his concepts as much while in the process of building as when he had been drawing in preparation for the project. Gaudí's drawings and his buildings, then, form two histories, distinct but interlocking.

20

CHRONOLOGY

Abridged chronology of the life and works of Antonio Gaudí

1852   June 25. Born in or near Reus (near Tarragona) of Francisco Gaudí y Serra and Antonia Cornet y Bertrán.

1873–78   Attended the Escuela Provincial de Arquitectura in Barcelona, where he became a matriculated student in 1874. Spent considerable time working for established architects and engineers, probably as draftsman.

1875/77–82   Assisted the *maestro de obras* José Fontseré with work in and around the Parque de la Ciudadela of Barcelona.

1876–79   As part of a diary, wrote on the aesthetics of architecture (a theory of ''ornamentation'') and wrote a separate short piece on the Catalan country house. In Municipal Museum, Reus.

1878   Designed a glass showcase for the glove manufacturer Esteban Comella for the Paris Exposition that opened in June of that year. While supervising the construction of this, Gaudí made the acquaintance of Eusebio Güell y Bacigalupi, later his prime patron.

1878   Designed a reliquary (Cat. No. 22), perhaps for José M. Bocabella, later his first patron at the Sagrada Familia church.

1878   March 15. Awarded the title of architect.

1878   March. Made a layout, in collaboration with his schoolmate Emilio Cabanyes Rabassa of Mataró, for workers' housing at the cooperative there; this was done for the Paris Exposition of 1878. Gaudí, a friend of the cooperative's director Salvador Pagés, had done work for this organization as early as 1874, and he continued to do so into the 1880s.

1878   May 14. Designed a model kiosk for Enrique Girosi de Sanctis of Mataró to be constructed of metal and glass at various spots in the city of Barcelona for sanitary and civic reasons. Apparently none was ever built.

1878   June. Prepared a lengthy memorandum to the municipal government concerning the urbanistic importance of street lights, accompanied by plans and a design. These lights now stand in three parts of Barcelona.

1878   July. Wall, gate, and a columned roof for the theater for Pablo Miró in the Barcelona suburb of San Gervasio. Demolished soon after.

1879   Designs for an allegorical cavalcade at Vallfogona de Riucorp (Tarragona) to celebrate the 256th anniversary of the death of Vicente García (1580–1623), a local priest and poet. The celebration was held, but not Gaudí's cavalcade.

1880   In collaboration with the engineer José Serramalera designed elaborate electric lighting system for the Muralla de Mar section of the Barcelona waterfront. Not carried out.

1881   Published in *La Renaixensa* (vol. XI, nos. 51,53) his only known printed article, a review of the Exposition of Decorative Arts at the Institut del Foment del Treball Nacional in Barcelona.

1882   Supported Juan Martorell in the dispute over the rejection of Martorell's project for the completion of the façade and cupola of Barcelona Cathedral. Prepared a rendering of the project for *La Renaixensa*.

1883   July. Designed altar for the Chapel of the Holy Sacrament in the parochial church of Alella near Barcelona. Not constructed.

1883   Nov. On the nomination of Juan Martorell—who had himself turned it down—was commissioned to replace Francisco de Paula del Villar y Lozano as architect of the new Templo Expiatorio de la Sagrada Familia in Barcelona, a project that occupied Gaudí until his death.

1883–85   House for Manuel Vicens on what is now calle de las Carolinas, Barcelona. Occupied with some details until 1888.

1883–85   Summer villa "El Capricho" for Máximo Diaz de Quijano, son-in-law of the first Marqués de Comillas beside the latter's estate in Comillas (Province of Santander).

c.1884–87   Work on the Güell estate "Finca Güell" in Las Corts de Sarriá, a suburb of Barcelona. The stables, their gatehouse, and the famous dragon gate survive and have now been restored as the premises of the Cátedra de Gaudí of the Universidad Politécnica de Barcelona by its incumbent, Professor Juan Bassegoda.

1886–89   "Palacio Güell," new city residence of Eusebio Güell on the calle Conde del Asalto, Barcelona. It served as headquarters and archive of the Amigos de Gaudí of Barcelona from 1952 until 1969, when they were evicted by the Theater Museum installed there.

1887–94   Work on the Episcopal Palace at Astorga (Province of León) for the then Bishop, originally of Reus. Gaudí's work stopped shortly after the death of the bishop in 1893; the work was resumed under other supervision in the early 1900s. Recently the building has been excellently restored as the Museo de los Caminos.

1888–90   Colegio (school) de Santa Teresa de Jesus in the Barcelona suburb of Bonanova for Enrique de Ossó, founder of the order.

1891–94   León, "Casa de los Botines," an office and apartment block on the Plaza de San Marcelo for business associates of the Güell family; named after the founder of the firm.

1892–93	Designed, on commission for the second Marqués de Comillas, a Spanish Franciscan Mission in Tangier where he had traveled with the Marqués in 1887. Never built, although many drawings were made of which one small photograph survives (Cat. No. 79).
1898–1904	Occupied with an apartment building and adjoining business premises for the sons of Pedro Mártir Calvet, on c. Caspe, Barcelona. Mostly finished by 1899 when it won the first annual building prize to be awarded by the Ayuntamiento of Barcelona.
1898-c.1915	Engaged in work on the church for the workers' colony of the Güell textile factory at Santa Coloma de Cervelló, southwest of Barcelona.
1900–06	Made designs for changes in the exterior of the Sanctuary of the Misericordia in Reus. Not executed.
1900–08	"Bell Esguard," a villa in the Barcelona suburb of Bonanova, built beside the ruins of the ancient country residence of King Martín "el Humano" of Aragon.
1900–14	Laid out and constructed the Park Güell on the slopes of Monte Carmelo in Barcelona for Eusebio Güell. Designed in the manner of an English residential park with sites for approximately 60 homes, the project was unsuccessful and in 1922 was acquired by the municipality as a public park.
1901–02	Wall and gate of the *finca* (estate) of Hermenegildo Miralles in the suburb of Las Corts de Sarriá. The house and other structures were built afterwards by Domingo Sugrañes.
1901–15	Interior reform of the Cathedral of Palma de Mallorca for Bishop Pedro Campins. Unfinished.
1904	Workshop for the builder José Badía in Barcelona.
1904–06	Remodeling of the building at Paseo de Gracia 43, Barcelona, for the José Batlló y Casanovas family. Popularly known as the "Casa de los huesos."
1906	Made drawings for a viaduct (dedicated to the Barcelona Saint Eulalia) over the arroyo of Pomaret high above the city of Barcelona. Not executed.
1906–10	"La Pedrera," apartment building at Paseo de Gracia 92, Barcelona, for Doña Rosario Segimón de Milá.
1910	April 15–June 30. Exhibition of models, photographs, and drawings of Gaudí's work at the Société Nationale des Beaux-Arts in Paris. Expenses paid by Eusebio Güell.
1910–15	Gaudí began to withdraw from all secular commissions.
1918	July 8. Gaudí's patron, Eusebio Güell, died.
1926	June 7. Gaudí struck by trolley car near the Plaza de Tetuán while on his way from the Sagrada Familia site to worship at the church of S. Felipe Neri in the old quarter of Barcelona.
1926	June 10. Gaudí dies in the Hospital de Santa Cruz. He was buried on the 12th of June by special dispensation in the crypt of the Sagrada Familia church.

CATALOGUE

Note: In the final arrangement of the exhibition it was decided not to include, for various reasons, some of the drawings listed in the catalogue.

In the entries that follow, "Barcelona School of Architecture" refers to the Escuela Técnica Superior de Arquitectura de la Universidad Politécnica de Barcelona; "Sugrañes bequest" refers to the bequest of Gaudí's associate Domingo Sugrañes to the Municipal Museum in Reus. All measurements give the gross size of the entire sheet, height preceding width.

PROJECTS FROM ARCHITECTURAL SCHOOL (1873–78)

1   **Topographic Survey of the Riera de Malla, Barcelona.** c. 1874–76. India ink and watercolor on stiff drawing paper. 70.5 x 98.5 cm. Signed by the professor, A. Font, and by all participating students, including Gaudí. Barcelona School of Architecture.

2   **Extracted Historical Data for the Decoration of the Supports of the Philadelphia Exposition** (?). "Estracto de los asuntos históricos para la decoración de los soportes de la F. E." c. 1875–76. Lead pencil on rag paper. 31.5 x 21.5 cm. Municipal Museum, Reus (Sugrañes bequest).
If "F. E." stands for "Filadelfia Exposición," this is a study for the "Spanish Pavilion in the Exposition in Philadelphia" mentioned by Gaudí's biographer Ráfols. The inscription, probably taken from an epic Catalan poem, includes a reference to Filadelfia in Asia Minor.

3–4   **Patio of a Provincial Capitol Building.** 1876. Project for Gaudí's second course in design, 1875–76. Signed and dated 6 Oct. 1876; countersigned and approved by A. Font, 16 Sept. 1876. Barcelona School of Architecture.

3   Plan: composite plan of skylight and stairs. Black India ink on heavy coated paper. 59 x 44.5 cm. Scale 1/100.

4   Detail of elevation. Gouache and watercolor on thick watercolor paper. 76 x 50.5 cm.

5–8 **Embarcation Pier.** 1876. Project for school competition. Drawings signed by Gaudí and by the secretary of the judging tribunal, the architect Luis Doménech y Montaner. Barcelona School of Architecture.

5 Sketch *(esquisse).* 19 Oct. 1876. India ink with watercolor on watercolor paper. 48 x 63 cm.

6 Elevation: 21 Oct. 1876. India ink with watercolor on stiff drawing paper. 63 x 95.5 cm. Scale 1/100.

7 Site plan, with coded description of parts at lower left. 8 Nov. 1876. India ink on heavy glazed paper. 47.5 x 62.0 cm. Scale 1/1000.

8 Detail of interior. Undated. Watercolor on watercolor paper. 97 x 64.5 cm. Scale 1/10.

9 **Monumental Fountain for the Plaza de Cataluña in Barcelona.** 1877. Plan. Lead pencil on stiff drawing paper. 49 x 90.5 cm. Scale 1/250. Signed. Barcelona School of Architecture.

10 **General Hospital for Barcelona.** 1877. Ink notes and pencil sketches on both sides of notebook paper. 20.5 x 13.5 cm. Municipal Museum, Reus (Sugrañes bequest).
One side has notes on the cost per bed, in francs, of various foreign hospitals (including the Boston Free Hospital) with sketchy diagrammatic plans of hospitals laid out in pavilions. Other side has notes (by the page) from an unknown book and a small bed-layout of a hospital floor. Nothing is known of the final physical nature of this project listed by Ráfols as a school project.

11–15 **"Paraninfo" (Academic Auditorium).** 1877. Gaudí's thesis project in his final year. Drawings signed by Gaudí and countersigned by A. Font in Oct./Nov. 1877. Barcelona School of Architecture.

11 Sketch *(esquisse).* Lead pencil on stiff drawing paper. 50 x 62.5 cm.

12 Plan. Colored pencil on stiff drawing paper. 47 x 58.5 cm. Scale 1/100.

13 Transverse section. Watercolor on stiff drawing paper. 65 x 90.5 cm. Scale 1/50.

14 Longitudinal section. Watercolor and gouache on stiff drawing paper. 65.5 x 116.5 cm.

15 Detail: elevation and section of the seat of honor. Watercolor on stiff drawing paper. 151 x 84.5 cm. Scale 1/5.

16 **Gates and Fencing for the Parque de la Ciudadela of Barcelona.** Elevation. 30 May 1876. India ink on linen. 45.5 x 93.5 cm. Scale: 1/25. Instituto Municipal de Historia, Barcelona. Drawn by Gaudí as a student assistant to José Fontseré who signed the drawing as architect of the park.

DRAWINGS OF THE FIRST YEAR AS A TITLED ARCHITECT (1878)

17   **Showcase for Esteban Comella,** Barcelona glove-maker, for the Paris Universal Exposition of 1878 (opened in June). Elevation, with section and plan lightly traced. Pencil with white and blue gouache on reverse of Gaudí's business card. 7.7 x 11.8 cm. Municipal Museum, Reus (Sugrañes bequest).

18   **Model Kiosk** designed for Enrique Girosi de Sanctis, an inventor. Elevation and plan. 14 May 1878. India ink on very fine vegetable parchment. 80 x 70 cm. Scale 1/25. Signed. Instituto Municipal de Historia, Barcelona. These kiosks were to be a combination of restrooms, flower stalls, and billboards, constructed of iron and glass. Apparently none was built.

19–20 **Street Lights.** Drawn in connection with a memorandum of June 1878 to the city government of Barcelona concerning the design of new street lights. India ink on linen. 22 x 18 cm. Scale 1/300. Signed. Archivo Administrativo Municipal, Barcelona.

19   Disposition No. 1: Plan for siting of two lamps for the Plaza Real, Barcelona. 14 January 1879. Accepted 31 January 1879, and subsequently executed.

20   Disposition No. 2: Plan for four lamps for the same site (rejected). 14 January 1879.

21   **Wall and gate for a theater** for Pablo Miró in the Barcelona suburb of San Gervasio. Elevation. 30 July 1878. India ink on linen. 9.5 x 23.8 cm. Scale 1/50. Signed. Barcelona School of Architecture.

22   **Reliquary.** Elevation. 1878. Green, blue, and white watercolor on thick watercolor paper. 36 x 22 cm. Life size. Signed. Municipal Museum, Reus (Sugrañes bequest).

WORK FOR THE SOCIEDAD COOPERATIVA DE MATARÓ (c.1874–1883)

This early Spanish effort at socialism was established 7 July 1864 in Mataró, just up the coast from Barcelona. Its textile factory was in the Gracia suburb of Barcelona until the society constructed new facilities in Mataró in 1874–75 and moved there *in toto.* The enterprise sold out to a private firm c.1900. Note that Nos. 25 and 26 were apparently exhibited in 1878 at the Universal Exposition in Paris.

23   **Workers' Housing.** Plan. 29 March 1878. Black and red ink on linen. 31 x 103 cm. Scale 1/200. Signed by Gaudí and Emilio Cabanyes Rabassa (his associate there); countersigned by Salvador Pagés, Director of the enterprise. Archivo Municipal, Mataró. Of the 30 one-story houses planned, only the two with detailed plans drawn in were constructed.

24   **House.** Plan and elevation as constructed. 29 March 1878. Red, blue, and black ink on linen. 54 x 32 cm. Scale 1/50. Signed as in No. 23. Archivo Municipal, Mataró.

25 **Social Center.** Elevations of garden and street façades and a sample iron porch column (never constructed). May 1878. Pen and ink with watercolor on stiff drawing paper. 59 x 127.5 cm. Scale 1/50. Signed. Collection Miquel Brullet i Monmany, Mataró.

26 **Social Center.** Three plans: first floor, principal floor, semi-basement. May 1878. Pen and ink with watercolor on stiff drawing paper. 57.5 x 129.5 cm. Collection Miquel Brullet i Monmany, Mataró.

27 **Fence around the Society's property,** facing the calle de Iluro. 26 July 1878. Blue and black ink on linen. 23.5 x 62.5 cm. Scale 1/50. Signed. Archivo Municipal, Mataró.

28 **Site Plan with Two Buildings "A" and "B" in Elevation and Plan.** July 1883. Black, red, and blue on linen. 43 x 206 cm. Scale 1/200. Signed by Gaudí; countersigned by Pagés. Archivo Municipal, Mataró.

29 **Rear Elevations and Plans of Buildings "A" and "B."** July 1883. Black, red, and blue on linen. 52.5 x 124 cm. Scale 1/50. Signed by Gaudí; countersigned by Pagés. Archivo Municipal, Mataró.

30 **Street Elevation of Building "A" (the Entrance Pavilion).** 10 July 1883. 42.5 x 59.5 cm. Scale 1/50. Signed by Gaudí. Archivo Municipal, Mataró.

UNEXECUTED EARLY PROJECTS

31–35 **Studies for an Allegorical Cavalcade at Vallfogona de Riucorp.** [1879.] The cavalcade was not performed, although the celebration of which it was to have been a part took place and was even reported in New York.

31 Preliminary sketch, with added details of two figures and a monogram "V" in upper part. This served as a basis for No. 32 and others of the series. Silverpoint on wove paper. 15.5 x 24 cm. Signed on back. Municipal Museum, Reus (Sugrañes bequest).

32 "La Sega" (grain harvest). India ink on vegetable parchment. 17.5 x 36 cm. Signed by Gaudí (in Catalan). Amigos de Gaudí, Barcelona.

33 "La Vrema" (Ampurdense dialect for *la verema,* the harvest of grapes). India ink on vegetable parchment. 18 x 34.5 cm. Same signature. Amigos de Gaudí, Barcelona.

34 "La recolecció del Oli" (collecting oil). India ink on vegetable parchment. 17.5 x 34 cm. Same signature. Amigos de Gaudí, Barcelona.

35 No title. A less finished drawing for either the head or tail of the procession. India ink on vegetable parchment. 17.5 x 42.5 cm. Same signature. Amigos de Gaudí, Barcelona.

36 **Aerial Perspective of the Muralla de Mar.** Part of a project for the illumination of the Barcelona waterfront with monumental light fixtures, designed in collaboration with the engineer Serramalera in March 1880. Lead pencil on reverse of a large printed business card bearing Gaudí's name and address. 13.5 x 24 cm. Unsigned. Amigos de Gaudí, Barcelona.

37 Catedral de Barcelona: fatxada. 1882. Rendering by Gaudí of the project of his mentor Juan Martorell for the completion of the façade and western lantern of the Cathedral of Barcelona. Ink and watercolor on stiff drawing paper. 99 x 51 cm. No scale. Unsigned. Colegio Oficial de Arquitectos de Cataluña y Baleares, Barcelona (Colección Martorell).
The labeling is by the architect Luis Doménech y Montaner, who also reproduces the escutcheon he had earlier designed as a logo for the Barcelona journal *La Renaixensa,* which in turn reproduced this façade rendering as a broadside sent to its subscribers and paid for by Eusebio Güell. Martorell's suggested project had lost out to that of Augusto Font, a teacher of Gaudí in architectural school. This rendering was produced for the ensuing dispute.

38 Proyecto de Capilla del SS. Sacramento para la Iglesia Parroquial de S. Félix de Alella. Elevation. July 1883. India ink on linen; drawn in reverse, apparently for some system of reproduction. 62.5 x 41.5 cm. Scale 1/25. Signed by Gaudí; countersigned by the Bishop of Barcelona, 11 March 1886. Archivo Parroquial, Alella.

WORKS OF THE 1880s

39–46 Barcelona, Casa Vicens. 1883–85. India ink on linen. Archivo Municipal de Gracia, now in the Biblioteca Central, Barcelona.

39 Façade. 15 Jan. 1883. 17 x 23.5 cm. Scale 1/100. Signed by Gaudí; countersigned and approved by M. Vicens Montaner, 10 March 1883.

40 Site plan. 15 January 1883. 23.5 x 15 cm. Scale 1/500. Similarly signed.

41 Plan of house. 15 Jan. 1883. 23.5 x 15 cm. Scale 1/50. Similarly signed.

42 Section of house façade. 15 Jan. 1883. 23 x 12 cm. Scale 1/50. Similarly signed.

43 Elevation and section of cascade in the garden. Aug. 1883. 28 x 82 cm. Scale 1/50. Signed by Gaudí; countersigned and approved by M. Vicens 27 Sept. 1883.

44 Plan of cascade. Aug. 1883. 28 x 82 cm. Scale 1/50. Similarly signed.

45 Section A–A of cascade. Aug. 1883. 28 x 32 cm. Scale 1/50. Similarly signed.

46 Section B–B of cascade. Aug. 1883. 28 x 72 cm. Scale 1/50. Similarly signed.

47–59 Barcelona, Palacio Güell. 1886–89.
Nos. 47–52 are early designs in India ink and red watercolor on linen, all on a common scale of 1/50. Signed and dated 30 June 1886; countersigned by Eusebio Güell. Archivo Administrativo Municipal, Barcelona. These simple plans do not provide for the rear wing that supported a terrace at the level of the principal floor, as is indicated in the measured drawings (see Nos. 53, 55).

47   Façade and section of façade. 57 x 64.5 cm.

48   Plan of basements. 47.5 x 67.5 cm.

49   Plan of ground floor. 47.5 x 64.5 cm.

50   Plan of mezzanine. 47.5 x 64.5 cm.

51   Plan of principal floor. 72 x 93 cm.

52   Plan of second floor. 47.5 x 65 cm.

Nos. 53–59 are seven large sheets printed from measured drawings of the Palacio Güell that Eusebio Güell had prepared for the Gaudí exhibition of 1910 in Paris. Unsigned; labeled in French and Catalan. Catalan Archive, Columbia University, New York.

53   Section a–b. 55 x 36.5 cm. Scale 1/150.

54   Plans of basement, street floor, mezzanine, principal floor. 55 x 36.5 cm. Scale 1/250.

55   Plans of the second floor, annex to salon, third floor, roof terrace. Scale 1/250.

56–59   Column elevations. 40 x 60 cm.

60–68 **Astorga, Episcopal Palace.** 1887–94. Nine blueprints of the original plans, now lost, that Gaudí submitted in 1887 to the Real Academia de San Fernando in Madrid. The Academy took two years to approve the plans, and the building was not carried out exactly as represented in the drawings. All are signed by Gaudí and dated 1887. Museo de los Caminos (in the former Episcopal Palace), Astorga.

60   Exterior elevation, SE. 42 x 58.5 cm. Scale 1/100.

61   Exterior elevation, NW. 42 x 55 cm. Scale 1/100.

62   Site plan. 42 x 57 cm. Scale 1/500.

63   Plan of semi-cellar. 57 x 41.5 cm. Scale 1/100.

64   Plan of lower floor. 57.5 x 42 cm. Scale 1/100.

65   Plan of principal floor. 56 x 42 cm. Scale 1/100.

66   Plan of attic. 59.5 x 41.5 cm. Scale 1/100.

67   Transverse section. 42 x 54.5 cm. Scale 1/100.

68   Various details and minor sections. Overall 42 x 51.5 cm. Various scales.

WORKS OF THE 1890s

69–78 **León, Casa de los Botines.** 1891–94. Two measured drawings (Nos. 69 and 70) were placed in the base of the statue of St. George on the façade of the building in 1893; recovered when the statue was temporarily removed in the early 1950s, they are now owned by the bank that owns the building, the Caja de Ahorros de León. Also preserved are a number of working drawings, all done in ink on linen and on a scale of 1/10 (Nos. 71–78), now in the collection of the Amigos de Gaudí, Barcelona.

69 Elevation. Labeled "Proyecto de la casa de los Señores Fernández y Andrés," with a poised lion inscribed "Léon." Dec. 1891. India ink on linen. 61 x 63 cm. Scale 1/100. Signed by Gaudí, countersigned by both owners and approved 21 Dec. 1891.

70 Plan. Dec. 1891. India ink on linen. 65 x 62.5 cm. Scale 1/100. Similarly labeled and signed. The brown stain in the drawing is from seepage in its lead receptacle under the statue.

71 "Torre de angulo..." Elevations and sections. 138 x 94 cm.

72 "Detalle de la fachada..." Elevation and section. 142.5 x 67 cm.

73 "Ventana de 2 y 3 pisos..." Elevations and sections. 98 x 40 cm.

74 "Conjunto de la situacion de los 'Tacs'..." Elevations and sections. 80 x 15 cm.

75 "Puertas de entrada..." Elevation, plan, sections. 100.5 x 53.5 cm.

76 Interior Woodwork. Elevation. 48 x 129 cm.

77 Interior Woodwork and Staircase. Elevation, with small sketch at right. 48 x 128.5 cm.

78 "Detalle de carpintería..." Elevation, plan, and section. 107.5 x 94.5 cm.

79 **Misiones Católicas de Africa—Tanger.** Elevation and small plan. 1892–93. Postcard photograph dedicated by Gaudí to D. Mariano Andrés, co-owner of the León building. 10.6 x 14.7 cm. Physical characteristics of the original not known. Along with many other drawings for this project of Franciscan Missions for the second Marqués de Comillas, it was lost in Gaudí's atelier in 1936. Other inscriptions on the photograph are illegible. Amigos de Gaudí, Barcelona.

80 **Barcelona, Paseo de Colón.** Small shed "covertizo provisional." Façade and plan. 7 July 1894. India ink on linen. 54 x 50.5 cm. Scale 1/50. Signed. Archivo Administrativo de Fomento del Ayuntamiento, Barcelona.

81 **Barcelona, calle Lancaster, no. 7.** Project for a room for water tanks to be constructed on the roof of a building owned by Eusebio Güell. Section and plan. 9 Feb. 1895. India ink on linen. 31 x 43.5 cm. Scale 1/100. Signed by Gaudí; countersigned by Eusebio Güell. Archivo Administrativo de Fomento del Ayuntamiento, Barcelona.

82   **Barcelona, calle Conde del Asalto, no. 9.** Project for doorman's residence on roof. Section and plan. April 1895. Red and black ink on linen. 31.5 x 40 cm. Scale 1/100. Signed by Gaudí; countersigned by Eusebio Güell. Archivo Administrativo de Fomento del Ayuntamiento, Barcelona.

83   **Barcelona, Rambla de Capuchinos, no. 30.** Project for laundry facility to be erected on the roof of a building owned by Eusebio Güell. Elevation and plan. April 1895. Red and black ink on linen. 31.5 x 73 cm. Signed by Gaudí; countersigned by Eusebio Güell. Archivo Administrativo de Fomento del Ayuntamiento, Barcelona.

84   **Barcelona, calle Códols, no. 16.** Project for laundry facilities to be erected on the roof of a building owned by Eusebio Güell. Siting, section, plan, and elevation. 1897. India ink on linen. 55 x 22.5 cm. Scale 1/50. Signed by Gaudí; countersigned by Eusebio Güell. Archivo Administrativo de Fomento del Ayuntamiento, Barcelona.

85–87   **Barcelona, calle del Escorial.** Project for house for painter Alejo Clapés (friend of Gaudí). Nov. 1899. Black and pink on linen. Scale 1/50. Signed by Gaudí; countersigned by Clapés.

85   Elevation. 48 x 70 cm.

86   Site plan and lower floor. 36 x 95 cm.

87   Upper floor plan. 37 x 47 cm.

88–98   **Barcelona, Casa Calvet.** 1898–1904. Two sets of plans exist for this building. One set, in Spanish, carries various official inscriptions, the signature of Gaudí, the countersignature of the proprietors ''Sucesores de Pedro M. (Mártir) Calvet,'' and the approval of the municipal architect. A second set, in Catalan and presumably for the owners, carries only the name of the house, type of plan, and scale; the Catalan plans seem to be slightly more complete and perhaps later (they are undated). All originals are ink on linen. They are in the possession of the heirs of Santiago Llensa de Gelcen, the present owners of the building.

88   Façade: elevation and section (Spanish only). 29 March 1898. 81 x 53 cm. Scale 1/50.

89   Modifications to façade, elevation (Spanish only). 24 Nov. 1898. 21 x 46 cm. Scale 1/50. Signed by Gaudí; countersigned by Eduardo Calvet.

90   Site plan (Spanish only). 19 Jan. 1897. 23 x 18 cm. Scale 1/500. Signed.

91   Building placement plan (Spanish only). 29 March 1898. 24 x 14 cm. Scale 1/500.

92, 93   Basement plan (Spanish & Catalan). Spanish version is dated 29 March 1898. Spanish, 41 x 110 cm; Catalan, 36 x 60 cm. Scale 1/50.

94, 95   Plan of lower floor (Spanish & Catalan). Spanish version is dated 29 March 1898. Spanish, 36 x 108 cm; Catalan, 37.5 x 104 cm. Scale 1/50.

96, 97 Plan of intermediate floors (Spanish & Catalan). Spanish version dated 29 March 1898. Spanish, 43 x 68 cm; Catalan, 40 x 61 cm. Scale 1/50.

98 Plan of roof terrace (Catalan only). 36 x 56 cm. Scale 1/50.

99 **Barcelona, Expiatory Church of the Sagrada Familia. Façade of the Nativity** (under construction 1893–1903). Two studies for the metal grille around the center column of the central portal of the Façade of the Nativity. Undated. Lead pencil on stiff drawing paper. 23 x 13 cm. No scale. Unsigned. Barcelona School of Architecture (Matamala Collection).

WORKS OF THE EARLY 1900s

100 **Reus, Sanctuary of the Misericordia.** Reform to the exterior of the existing church (not carried out). Two sketches of elevation and others of pier placement and vaulting. c. 1900–1906 (date in dispute). Lead pencil on manila paper. 19.5 x 24.5 cm. No scale. Unsigned. Municipal Museum, Reus (Sugrañes bequest).

101 **Barcelona, Villa Bell Esguard.** 1900–08. Plan. 20 Nov. 1905. India ink on linen. 59 x 138 cm. Scale 1/500. Signed. Archivo Administrativo Municipal de Fomento del Ayuntamiento, Barcelona.

102 **Barcelona, Park Güell.** 1900–14. Plan. Blueprint of original made for the contractor of the works. Undated. 74.5 x 57 cm. Scale 1/1000. Unsigned. Barcelona School of Architecture.

103 **Barcelona, wall for the Miralles estate.** 1901–02. Elevation of wall at 1/200; two sections of wall at 1/50; and site plan at 1/2000. 18 April 1902. Ink on linen. 32 x 152 cm. Signed by Gaudí; countersigned by the client, Hermenegildo Miralles. Collection Thaddeus E. Kusmierski, Berkeley.

104 **Barcelona, Talleres Badía.** A workshop for one of Gaudí's associates. Placement, façade, plan, section. 12 Aug. 1904. India ink on linen. 54.5 x 7.4 cm. Signed by Gaudí; countersigned by proprietor. Archivo Administrativo Municipal, Barcelona.

105-09 **Barcelona, Casa Batlló.** 1904-06. Reform of existing building.

105 Study of the façade, some sections, elements of plans, and unidentified details. 1904–05. Lead pencil on stiff drawing paper. 50 x 67.5 cm. Scale 1/50. Unsigned. Barcelona School of Architecture.
Most of the handwriting on the plan would seem to be that of Francisco Berenguer, Gaudí's assistant, as is perhaps the ruling out of the actual state of the original façade, over which Gaudí has drawn the details of the projected new façade. Some of the notations and larger numbers seem to be in Gaudí's hand, added as he worked on the sheet that Berenguer had prepared for him.

Nos. 106–09 are official drawings prepared to accompany the petition to alter the building. India ink on linen. Scale 1/100. Archivo Administrativo Municipal, Barcelona.

106 Elevation and section of façade, and plans. 24 Oct. 1904. 47.5 x 97.5 cm. Scale 1 / 100. Signed.

107 Terrace plan. 47.2 x 45.1 cm.

108 Plans of basement, street floor, principal floor. 63.1 x 85.8 cm.

109 Plan and section of basement. 33 x 89.3 cm.

110 Viaduct in honor of Sta. Eulalia de Barcelona (never constructed). Elevation, plan, section A–B. 1 Aug. 1906. India ink on linen. 58 x 210 cm. Scale 1 / 100. Signed. Archivo Municipal de Sarriá, now in the Biblioteca Central, Barcelona.

111-26 **Barcelona, Casa Milá.** 1906–10. There exist two early versions of the plans for this building, neither of which conforms very closely to the building as executed. One, somewhat freer and probably earlier, is a set of blueprints now in the possession of the heirs of César Martinell who received them from Francisco de Paula Quintana, one of Gaudí's close associates. The other is a set of outline drawings distributed among the Archivo Administrativo Municipal of Barcelona, the office of the present proprietors of the Casa Milá, and the Barcelona School of Architecture.
The blueprints (Nos. 111–19) are 35 x 26 cm, scale 1 / 200, unsigned and undated.

111 Basement plan.

112 Half-basement plan.

113 Ground floor plan.

114-18 Five upper-floor plans.

119 Section.

The official drawings are of various sizes; all but one are scaled 1 / 100. They are signed by Gaudí; countersigned by Milá (Feb. 1906), and approved by the municipality.

120 Placement. 39 x 23.5 cm. Scale 1 / 500.

121 Façade elevation. 58.5 x 93 cm.

122 Basement plan. 46 x 84 cm.

123 Ground-floor plan. 46.5 x 82.5 cm.

124 Third-floor plan. 46 x 83.5 cm.

125 Section. 53 x 44 cm.

126 Profile of attic arches. 35.5 x 89 cm.

127-28 **Santa Coloma de Cervelló, church for the Colonia Güell,** a textile workers' colony. 1898–c.1915. Only the crypt was built of the church Gaudí designed for the colony. There are several versions of the tinted drawings that Gaudí made for the exterior and interior of the building. They are based on the force-lines of the hanging funicular model he constructed, and in some cases they were actually drawn on inverted photographs of the model. These seem to date to c. 1906–10, when construction was about to start; first stone was laid in 1908, but little progress occurred before 1912.

127 Exterior. Gouache (now faded) on sepia heliographic print. 59.5 x 46.5 cm. Scale approx. 1/10. Unsigned. Collection Edmundo Vidal, Barcelona.

128 Interior. Gouache (now faded) on sepia heliographic print. 61 x 47.5 cm. Scale approx. 1/10. Unsigned. Collection Edmundo Vidal, Barcelona.

129 **Three sketches:** sprig of passion flower; passion flower leaves in a triangular frame; monogram with Maltese cross in center. Lead pencil on stiff drawing paper. 17 x 12 cm. Inscribed with ''A-G'' monogram and the date ''1911.'' One of numerous attributed drawings belonging to the sculptor Juan Matamala that were transferred in 1972 to the Barcelona School of Architecture.
Insofar as the ''A-G'' monogram signature is one that Gaudí had ceased using long before 1911, and the inscription of 1911 does not seem to be in his hand, it seems most likely that this sheet, bearing Gaudí's much earlier light sketch of the cruciform monogram, was re-used in 1911 by his associate Lorenzo Matamala (Juan's father) to sketch flowers for sculpture.

UNDATED DRAWINGS

130 **Marginal drawings, including sketch of a capital,** on four pages of school notes (for a surveying course?). Pencil and ink on ordinary notebook paper. Each sheet is 21 x 31 cm. Municipal Museum, Reus (Sugrañes bequest).

131 **Head of a Goat.** Attributed to Gaudí and dated after March 1878 by Ráfols who received it from him. Pencil and pastel on heavy tan drawing paper. 25 x 35 cm. Unsigned. Amigos de Gaudí, Barcelona.

132 **Plants.** Sketches on a sheet divided into quadrants. Ink on wove paper. 22 x 16.5 cm. Unsigned. Municipal Museum, Reus (Sugrañes bequest).

133 **Sketch of passion flower vine** on three separate sheets. Presumably for sculptured ornament. Lead pencil on stiff drawing paper. Each sheet is 12 x 17 cm. Unsigned. Barcelona School of Architecture (Matamala Collection).

134 **Sketch of flowers** on two separate, but apparently associated sheets. Lead pencil on stiff drawing paper. 17 x 15 cm and 17 x 25 cm. Both sheets have been folded. Unsigned. Barcelona School of Architecture (Matamala Collection).

135   **Sketch for a heraldic monogram,** probably to be sculpted: an ''M'' surmounted by Maltese cross. Blue stylographic pen on stiff drawing paper. 7.5 x 10.5 cm. Unsigned. Barcelona School of Architecture (Matamala Collection).

136   **Sketch for a monogram (''M'').** Blue stylographic pen on stiff drawing paper. 8 x 10 cm. Unsigned. Barcelona School of Architecture (Matamala Collection).

137   **Sketch for a monogram,** probably to be sculpted: an ''IHS'' with superimposed crown and floral spray. Indistinguishable sketch to the left. Blue stylographic pen on stiff drawing paper. 10.5 x 16.5 cm. Unsigned. Barcelona School of Architecture (Matamala Collection).

138   **Study for the crowning element of a standard,** composed of the letter ''M'' surmounted by a Maltese cross with flower(?) twisted around its base. Scribbles to the right. Blue stylographic pen on manila paper. 20 x 9 cm. Unsigned. Barcelona School of Architecture (Matamala Collection).

P   L D

5

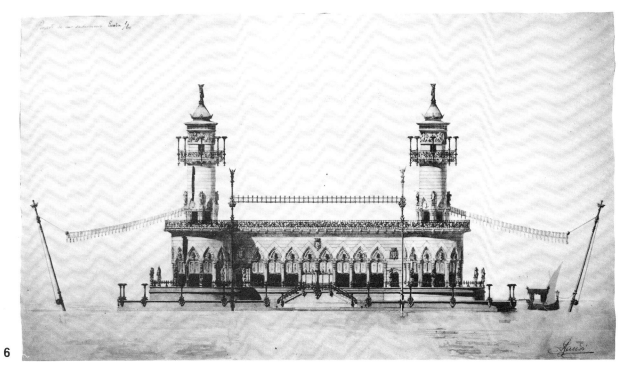

6

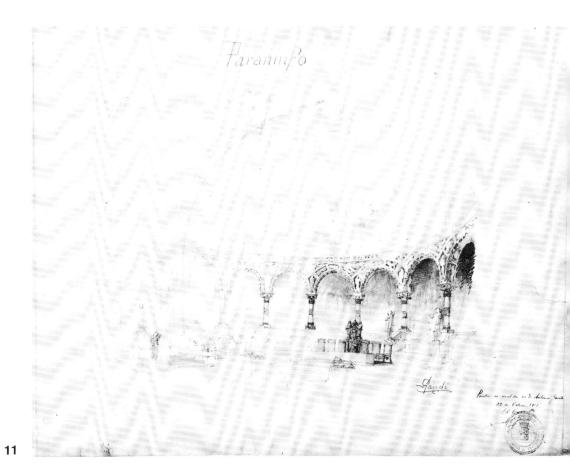

Paraninfo

11

13

15

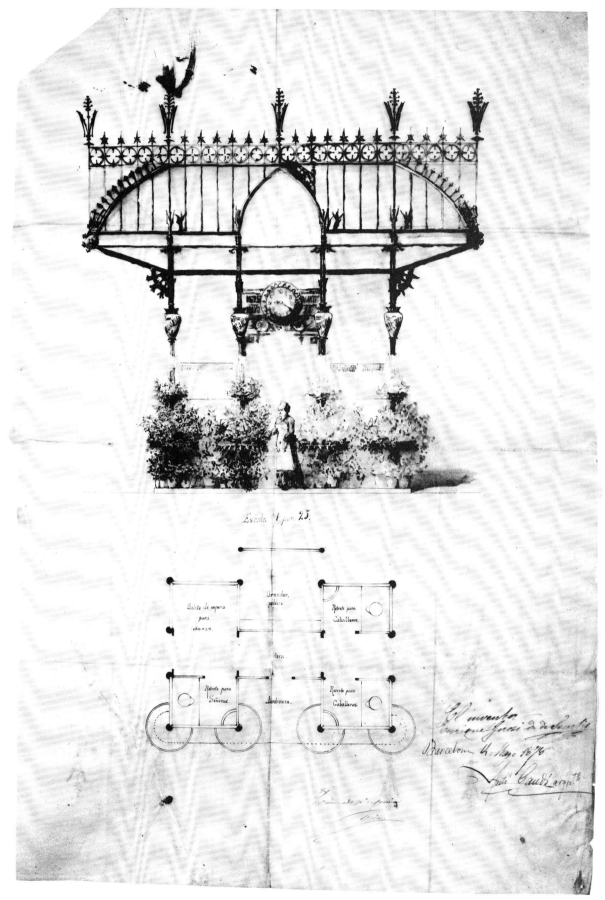

31

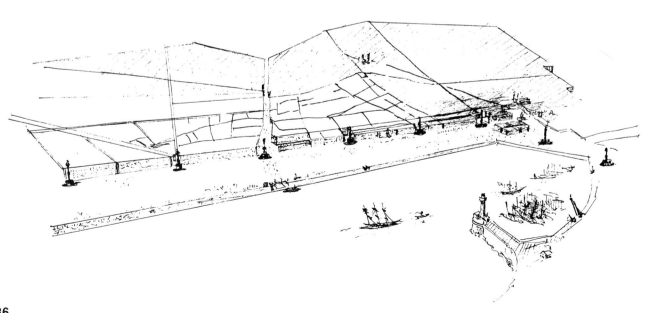

36

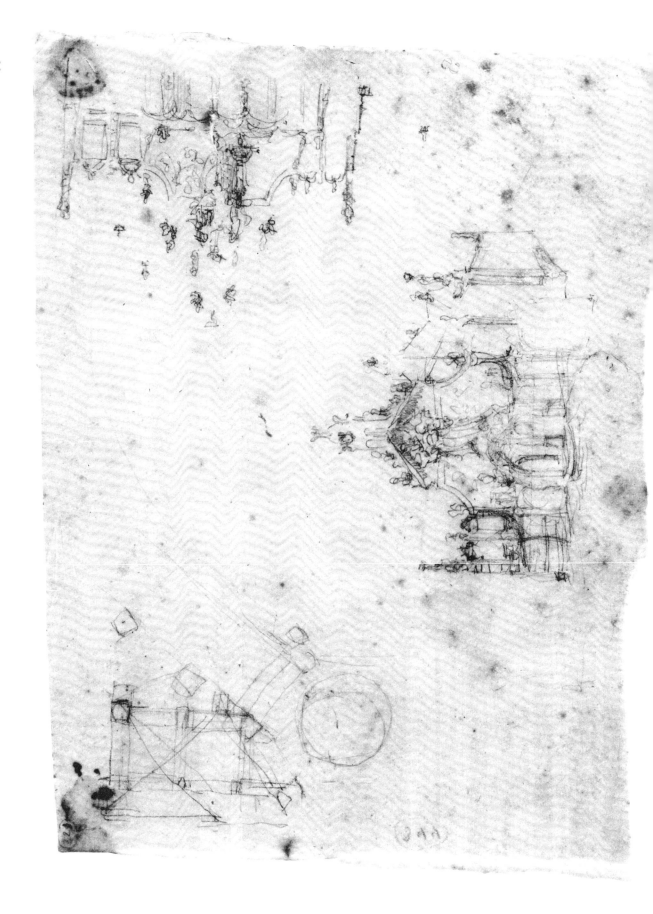

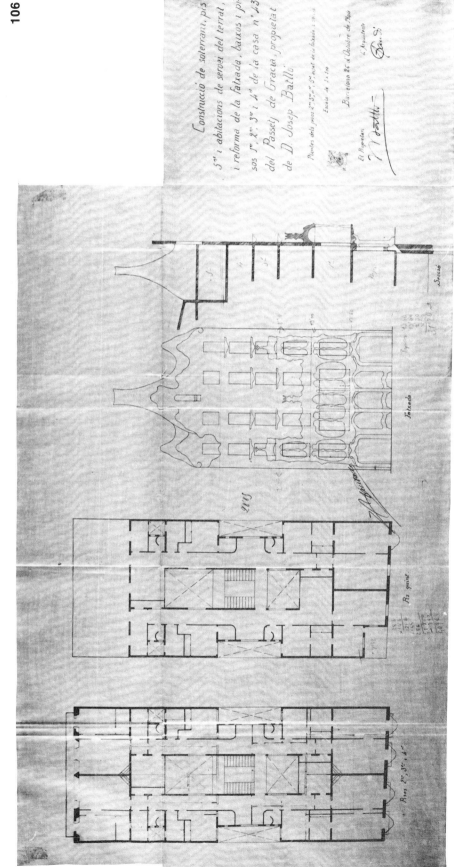

Construcció de soterrani, p.5
5 i ablacions de servei del terrat,
i reforma de la fatxada, baxos i p[r]
sos 1°, 2°, 3° i 4° de la casa n°43
del Passej de Gracia, propietat
de D Josep Batlló

Plantes dels pisos 1°, 3°, 4° i 5° al mat de la fatxada i b.n.o
Escala de 1×1m

Barcelona 26 d'Octubre de 190

El Propietari   L'Arquitecte

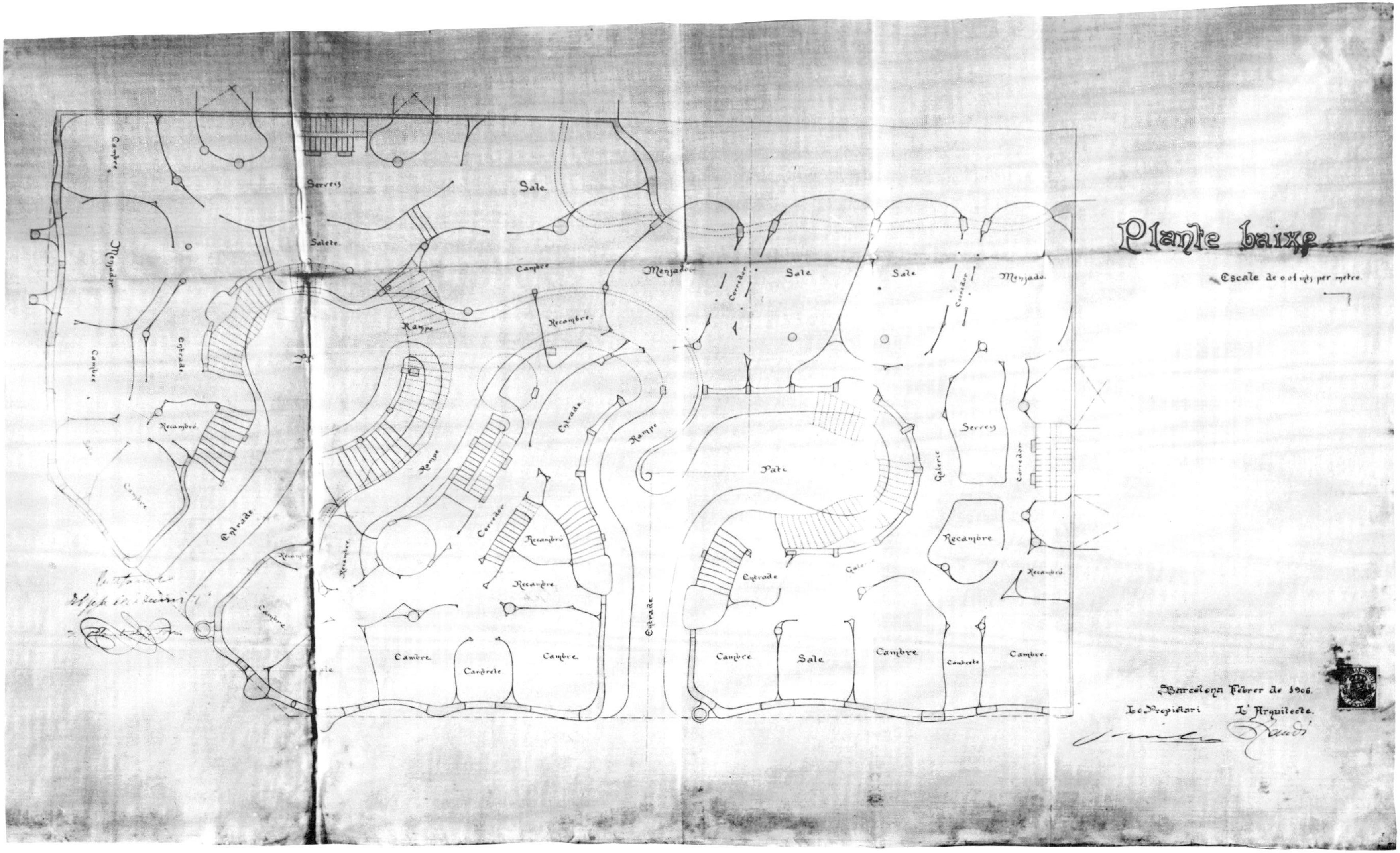
Plante baixe
Escale de 0.01 mts per metre.
Barcelona Febrer de 1906.
Lo Propietari
L' Arquitecte.
Gaudí
Sale
Serreys
Salete
Cambre
Menjador
Entrade
Recambre
Rampe
Corredor
Pati
Galerie
Cambrete
Menjado

130 (detail)

131